Tips for Reading Together

Children learn best when reading is fun.

- Talk about the title and the pictures on the cover.
- Look through the pictures together and discuss what you think the story might be about.
- Read the story together, inviting your child to read with you.
- Give lots of praise as your child reads with you, and help them when necessary.
- Try different ways of helping if they get stuck on a word. For example: refer to the picture, or read the first sound or syllable of the word, or read the whole sentence. Focus on the meaning.
- Have fun finding the hidden seashells.
- Re-read the story later, encouraging your child to read as much of it as they can.

Children enjoy re-reading stories and this helps to build their confidence.

Have fun!

Find the 10 seashells hidden in the pictures.

The Real Floppy

Written by Roderick Hunt
Illustrated by Alex Brychta

OXFORD

UNIVERSITY PRESS

The children ran onto the sand.

"Let's play here," said Biff.

Wilma threw a ball and
Floppy ran after it.

Floppy ran back with the ball.

Dad ran up. "Stop!" he said.

"Look at that," said Dad.

"Dogs can't go on the sand."

"Poor Floppy!" said Mum.

"I'll take him for a walk."

The children were upset.

They didn't want Floppy to go.

"Let's give Mum a surprise,"
said Dad.

They made a big pile of sand.
Everyone helped.

"Now let's pat it flat," said Dad.

"Let's make his head," said Biff.

"And his ears," said Chip.

"Let's put in his eyes," said Wilf.

"And make his tail," said Kipper.

Mum came back.

"Surprise! Surprise!" said Biff.

"A Floppy made of sand!"
said Mum.

"It's a good sand dog,"
said Kipper.

"But I love the real Floppy best."

Think about the story

Why wasn't Floppy allowed on the beach?

What was Mum's surprise? Why was it a good surprise?

Why were the children happy when they were making Mum's surprise?

What have you made out of sand? Were you proud of it?

Picture puzzle

How many things can you find beginning with the same sound as the 's' in sea?

(Answer to picture puzzle: sail, sand, sandcastle, sea, sunglasses)

More books for you to enjoy

Level 1:
Getting Ready

Level 2:
Starting to Read

Level 3:
Becoming a Reader

Level 4:
Building Confidence

Level 5:
Reading with Confidence

OXFORD
UNIVERSITY PRESS

Great Clarendon Street,
Oxford OX2 6DP

Text © Roderick Hunt 2005
Illustrations © Alex Brychta 2005
Designed by Andy Wilson

First published 2005
All rights reserved

British Library Cataloguing
in Publication Data available

ISBN 978-0-19-838561-5

10 9 8 7 6 5 4

Printed in China by Imago

Have more fun
with Read at Home

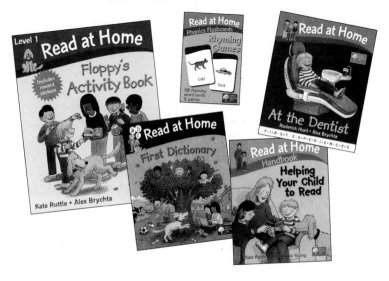